JEWISH BEDTIME STORIES and SONGS

From TORAH TIMES to the present day, gratitude is a strongly Jewish concept. Thankfulness may take an infinite number of forms, from a personal, quickly whispered "thank God" to a communal expression of gratitude.

The traditional synagogue morning service includes a series of *brachot* (blessings) entitled *Birchot HaShachar* ("Sunrise Blessings"), which is sometimes called *Nissim Kol Yom* ("Everyday Miracles"). This daily naming of things for which to be thankful was originally recited at home upon awakening and begins with gratitude that the rooster—an old-fashioned alarm clock—can distinguish night from day. The list includes appreciation to God for freedom, for sight, and for giving strength to the weary. These blessings also remind us to be grateful that our bodies function properly—from an "extraordinary head" to a "good bottom," a fact made splendidly clear in this book.

The Bible abounds with expressions of gratitude. Attributed to King David, Psalm 139 includes the words: "I praise You (God) because I am awesomely made. Your works are wonderful; I know this well." How important—and how Jewish!—for children to grow up recognizing themselves as amazing blessings to the world. *All of Me!* offers the opportunity to celebrate with our children the fact that every part of them is precious and that they, along with the adults who love them, are grateful for the awesome nature of their bodies and their lives.

SCHOLASTIC INC.

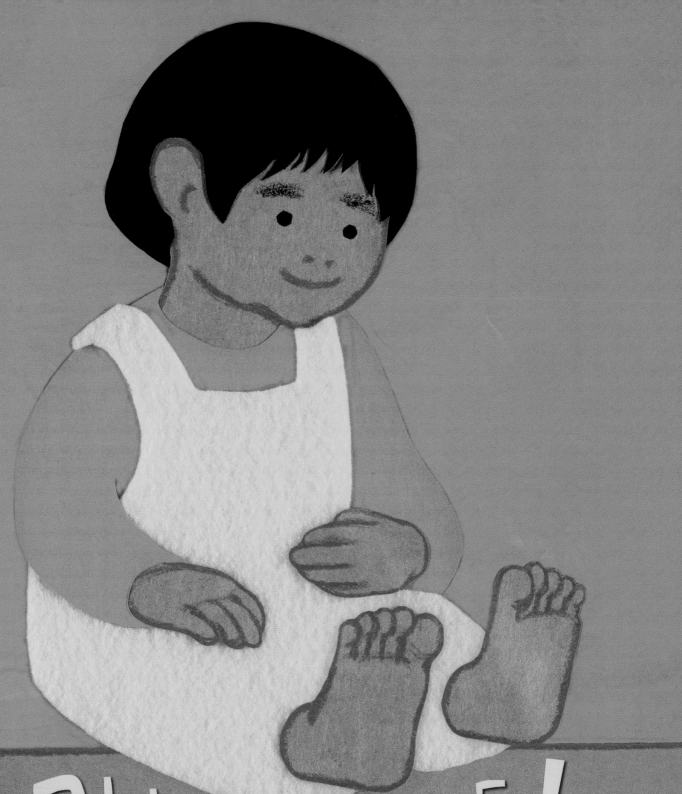

ALL OF ME!

a book of thanks

BY MOLLY BANG

10 9 8 7 6 5 4 3 2 1   10 11 12 13 14

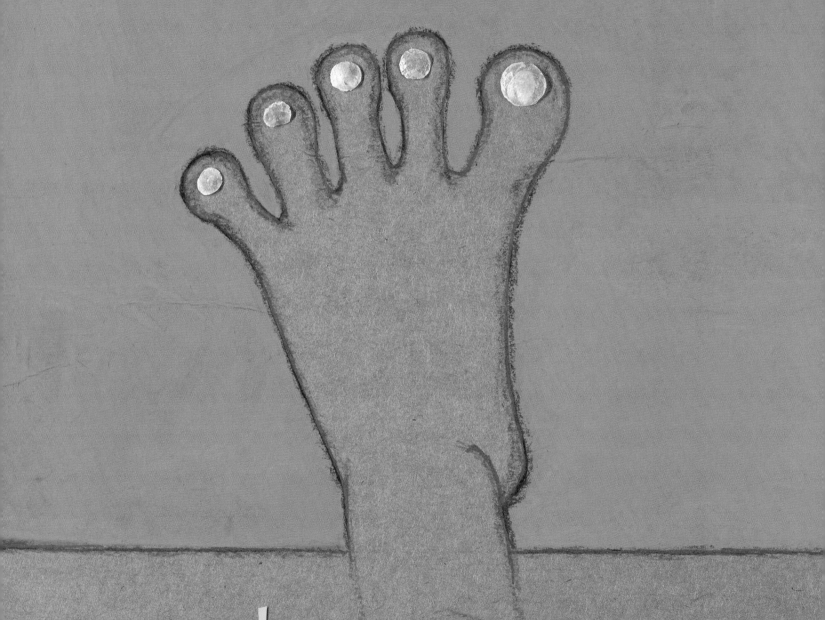

Look at my fine feet!
Thank you, feet,
for holding me up

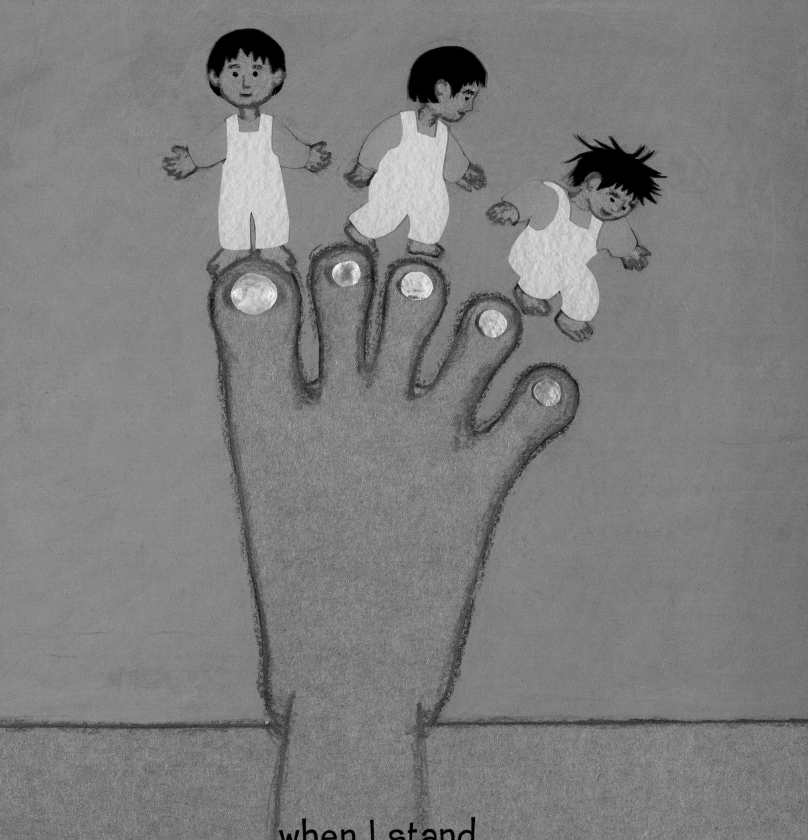

when I stand,
and when I walk,
and when I jump!

When I sit down, I sit on my good bottom.

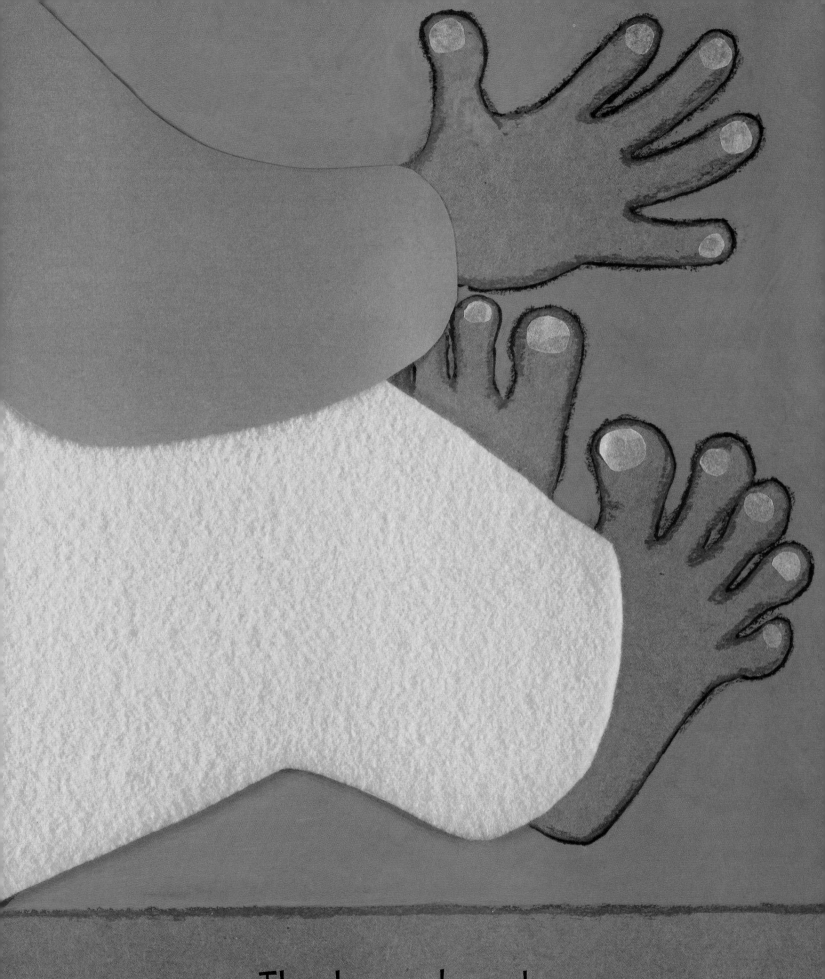

Thank goodness!

What grand hands!
Thank you, hands,
for gripping

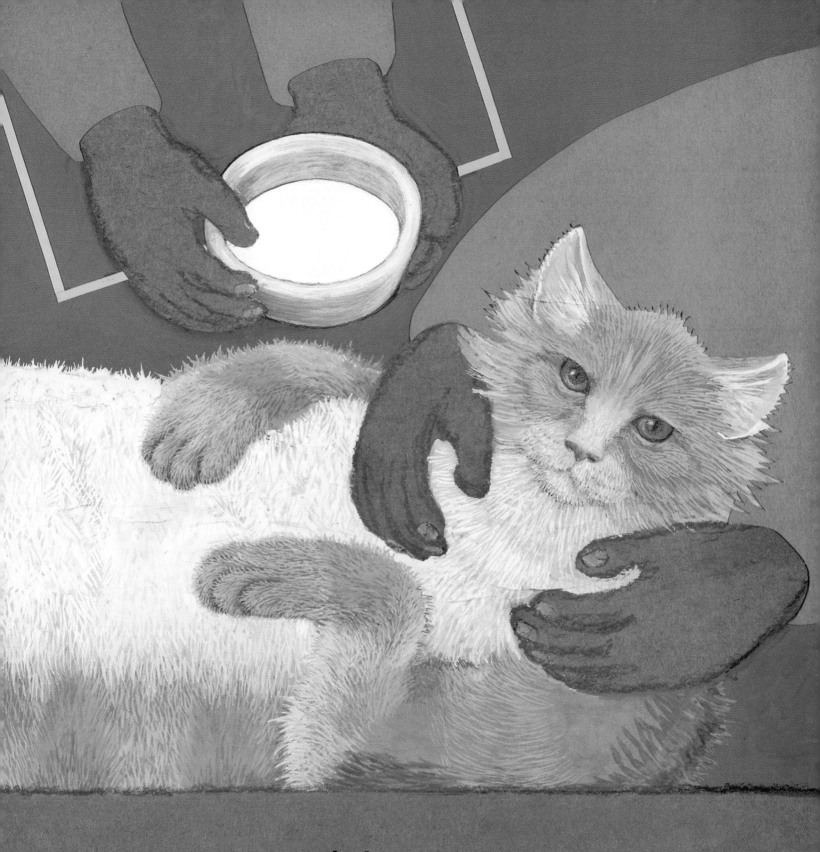

and throwing
and patting and holding.
And for hugging.

Thank you, arms,
for hugging even more.

And look at my knees and elbows!
My knees and elbows bend whenever I ask!

Now my hands feel here, up here.
I feel my head.

Thank you, my extraordinary head
and all your different parts.

I smile and talk and sing with my . . .
mouth.
My lips kiss Mommy and Daddy.

My teeth bite crackers. My tongue licks
ice cream. My mouth tastes all my food
before it slides down here, into my tummy.

I see with my . . .
eyes.
I see the night outside.

Inside I see light and animals, a ball,
a clock, a book, and big hands.
Whose big hands are those?

I smell with my . . . nose.
So many different smells!

(And sometimes my nose
rubs other noses.)

I listen with my . . .

ears.

Outside I hear cars rumbling.

I hear people playing music.

I hear honking, singing, barking,
and laughing. Inside I hear purring.
I hear a ticking clock.
And in between the noises, I hear . . .

SILENCE.

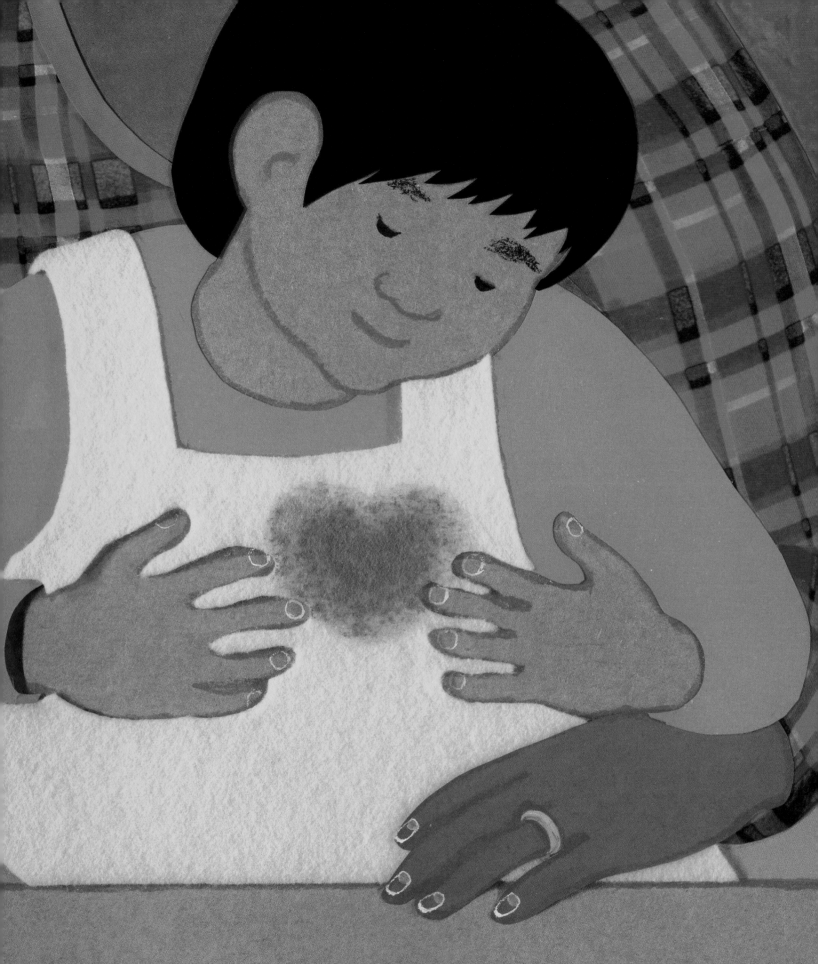

Now I feel my heart beat: thump, thump, thump.

Thank you, heart, for pumping life all through my body. Thank you, my whole body.

Today I did so many things.
Today I felt so many feelings.
I felt curious, and excited,

and angry, and brave, and sad,
and scared, and shy, and happy,
and thankful, and calm.

Today I feel loving—

loving and perfectly safe.

And right now I also know that I am part of this whole world — this universe!

All this is my home. I am ALIVE.
And this whole universe is inside . . .

. . . all of me! What a wonder.

BOOKS ARE FUN TO MAKE!

To make this book, I needed:

PAPER BAGS. (You have to use the inside, where there is no ink printed on the paper.)

CLOTH AND PAPER. I like to cut out pieces of cloth and construction paper with scissors and glue them onto the paper-bag paper. Some-times I cut out pictures from a magazine and paste them on, too.

CRAYONS!! I made thick, strong lines with red crayon. You can color in with crayons, too. I only used red, but of course you can use ALL the colors. I think I need a new red crayon.

PAINTS. I love paint. Some of my paint is in little jars. Some paint I squeeze from tubes into scallop shells I picked up from a beach in Nova Scotia.

PAINTBRUSHES. I guess I could have painted with my fingers or with a stick. But I like brushes.

WATER. You have to rinse the paint off your brush before you use a new color. If you don't rinse your brush in clean water, all the colors mix together, and everything turns muddy gray or brown.

Before I made any pictures, I first thought up the words. I had been thinking and thinking about this book for years, but finally one day all the words came sliding into my head. I don't know where they came from. Then I drew these "thumbnail" sketches with a pen to get an overall plan. (They're called that since the pictures are only about as big as my thumbnail.) Next, I pasted paper-bag paper onto thick boards and made the real pictures on that. After they were all done, I sent them to the publisher, who took photographs of them and added in my words. Then the books were printed and bound.

When you make your book, you can sew it, or glue it, or staple it all together. Don't forget to make a cover!

That's it!

What grand hands!

Paste a
handprint
here

_____   _____
NAME   DATE